THIS BOOK
BELONGS TO

_____

_____

_____

SIMPSONS COMICS 2014 ANNUAL

Copyright © 2013
Bongo Entertainment, Inc. and Matt Groening Productions, Inc. All rights reserved.
No part of this book may be used or reproduced in any manner whatsoever
without written permission except in the case of brief quotations
embodied in critical articles and reviews. For information address
Bongo Comics Group
P.O. Box 1963, Santa Monica, CA 90406-1963

Published in the UK by Titan Books, a division of Titan Publishing Group,
144 Southwark St., London SE1 0UP, under licence from Bongo Entertainment, Inc.

FIRST EDITION: SEPTEMBER 2013

ISBN 9781781167731

2 4 6 8 10 9 7 5 3 1

Publisher: Matt Groening
Creative Director: Nathan Kane
Managing Editor: Terry Delegeane
Director of Operations: Robert Zaugh
Art Director: Chia-Hsien Jason Ho
Art Director Special Projects: Serban Cristescu
Production Manager: Christopher Ungar
Assistant Art Director: Mike Rote
Assistant Editor: Karen Bates
Colors: Nathan Hamill, Art Villanueva
Administration: Ruth Waytz, Pete Benson
Editorial Assistant: Max Davison
Legal Guardian: Susan A. Grode

PRINTED IN ITALY

SiMPSONS COMICS
2014 ANNUAL

TITAN BOOKS

CHRIS BONHAM SCRIPT   **CHRIS HOUGHTON** ART   **NATHAN HAMILL** COLORS   **KAREN BATES** LETTERS   **NATHAN KANE** EDITOR

TEE-HEE!

¡GIGGLE!¡

YAAAH!

WHAT DID YOU DO NOW?

LISA! HELP!

KISS!

BART!

WIN!

BEEBER!

YAKETY SAX!

EARLIER THAT MORNING...

CLASS, AS YOU KNOW, TODAY IS OUR TRADITIONAL MISTLETOE RUN...

Mistletoe Run

...AN ANNUAL EVENT CREATED BY THE FOREFATHERS OF SPRINGFIELD TO ENSURE THAT THEIR SONS, NO MATTER HOW UGLY OR UNWASHED, WOULD EVENTUALLY LAND WIVES.

ALTHOUGH IT'S NOW STRICTLY SYMBOLIC, AS CITIZENS OF SPRINGFIELD, YOU'RE ALL LEGALLY BOUND TO PARTICIPATE.

BART! DID YOU FORGET?!?

NO WAY, MAN.

I REMOVED MY NAME FROM THE FISHBOWL. I DON'T TAKE CHANCES WHEN IT COMES TO COOTIES!

≳PHEW!≲

COOTIE FREE SINCE '03

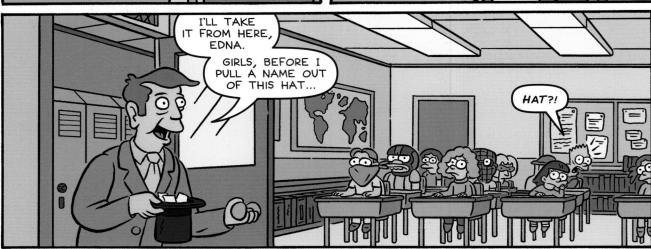

I'LL TAKE IT FROM HERE, EDNA.

GIRLS, BEFORE I PULL A NAME OUT OF THIS HAT...

HAT?!

...I WANT TO REVEAL THAT THE PRIZE FOR KISSING THIS YEAR'S BOY IS TWO TICKETS TO A *DUSTIN BEEBER* CONCERT!

EE EE!!!

OKAY...NO BIGGIE. THERE'S STILL A GOOD CHANCE MY NAME *WON'T* BE CALLED.

HMMM... PERHAPS I CAN KISS THE *OTHER* SIMPSON AT THIS SCHOOL AND WIN THE TICKETS!

♪ OH, ♪ LI-SA...!

NO.

LOOKS LIKE THEY'RE WEARING HIM DOWN.

GO, GIRLS, GO!

SEYMOUR, WHAT'S WITH THIS RIDICULOUS HAT? AND WHY DOES EVERY PAPER HAVE BART'S NAME ON IT?

FUNNY STORY. I DECIDED TO MANIPULATE THE EVENT AS PAYBACK FOR LAST WEEK'S *MASHED POTATO CATASTROPHE*.

GOOD FOR YOU, SEYMOUR.

SOON...

I THINK I GAVE THEM THE SLIP! IF I CAN JUST MAKE IT HOME, THE CONTEST IS OVER!*

*OBVIOUSLY BART IS PLAYING BY THE *REFORM* RULES THAT WERE ENACTED IN THE LATE EIGHTIES. —EDITOR NATHAN

HA! NICE TRY, LADIES! NO WOMAN CAN CATCH BART SIMPSON.

WHAT TH--?!

GOT YOU!

MWAH!

AH!

I GUESS MOM COOTIES AREN'T SO BAD.

HAPPY HOLIDAYS, MY SPECIAL LITTLE GUY!

NO FAIR!

BUT THE TICKETS!

AT LEAST I WON'T HAVE TO GO TO THAT STUPID CONCERT SINCE YOU WON, MOM!

RIGHT?

EVENTUALLY...

OH, BART! DUSTIN BEEBER IS THE CUTEST! COULDN'T YOU JUST DIE?

YOU SAID IT!

END

KIDS, THE LIGHTS ARE TANGLED ON SOMETHING. CAN YOU TAKE A LOOK?

SURE THING, DAD.

GRAMPA?! WHAT ARE YOU DOING IN THERE??

TRYING TO STOP ANOTHER *WAR OF THE WORLDS*, THAT'S WHAT!

YOU SEE, PUTTING LIGHTS ON HOUSES ISN'T A HUMAN CUSTOM...IT'S THE WORK OF *ALIENS!*

GRAMPA'S CHRISTMAS ORIGINS
Christmas Lights

"IT WAS CHRISTMAS EVE, 1947, IN THE DESERT TOWN OF ROSWELL, NEW MEXICO..."

AFTER MANY MONTHS ON THIS GODFORSAKEN PLANET, WE FINALLY HAVE ENOUGH POWER TO LIGHT OUR SHIP'S S.O.S. BEACON!

AT LAST!

SCHLUNK!

I AM SENDING THE SIGNAL! CROSS YOUR TENTACLES!

WOW!

IT IS GLORIOUS! OUR LIGHTS WILL BE SEEN DEEP INTO THE FARTHEST REACHES OF THE UNIVERSE!

THAT'S QUITE THE *HOLIDAY DISPLAY* YOU'VE GOT ON THE OL' HOMESTEAD!

YES.. "DISPLAY"...

ERIC ROGERS
SCRIPT

JOHN COSTANZA
PENCILS

PHYLLIS NOVIN
INKS

NATHAN HAMILL
COLORS

KAREN BATES
LETTERS

NATHAN KANE
EDITOR

GIFT EXCHANGE

WHAT'S EVERY-BODY ALL DRESSED UP FOR? AW...DON'T TELL ME THEY MOVED CHURCH TO FRIDAYS NOW.

YOU'D BETTER GET DRESSED, HOMER. TONIGHT IS NED FLANDERS' *ANNUAL CHRISTMAS SOCIAL*.

BUT I WAS GETTING READY TO FALL ASLEEP ON THE COUCH WITH THE TV ON!

I'M SURE HE'LL HAVE HIS SPECIAL HOLIDAY BUFFET AND COOKIE TABLE AGAIN.

WOO-HOO! FREE PIG-OUT AT FLANDERS' HOUSE! ALL RIGHT!

LOOK OUT, STRETCHY PANTS! IT'S PARTY TIME!

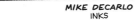

CHRIS YAMBAR
SCRIPT

PHIL ORTIZ
PENCILS

MIKE DECARLO
INKS

NATHAN HAMILL
COLORS

KAREN BATES
LETTERS

NATHAN KANE
EDITOR

HOMER, CAN YOU PROMISE TO **BEHAVE** TONIGHT? NED TRIES TO THROW A NICE PARTY EVERY YEAR, AND EVERY YEAR YOU SEEM TO RUIN IT.

HEY! HOW WAS I TO KNOW THOSE ANTIQUE SILVER SERVING BOWLS WEREN'T **TO GO** CONTAINERS? THEY **DID** HAVE LITTLE LIDS, Y'KNOW!

BESIDES, FLANDERS BOUGHT THEM BACK AT OUR SUMMER GARAGE SALE. WHERE DO YOU THINK ALL THAT EMERGENCY ICE CREAM MONEY CAME FROM?

NOW, LET'S GET GOING BEFORE EVERYONE ELSE SHOWS UP. WE DON'T WANT FLANDERS TO RUN OUT OF FOOD BEFORE WE GET THERE. I'LL GRAB MY COAT.

OHHHH...

NOT TO WORRY, MARGE. I'LL BE ON MY **BEST** BEHAVIOR!

ONE PAIR OF PANTS LATER...

AN EXCELLENTLY DECORATED HOME, MY GOOD MAN. PLEASE POINT ME TO YOUR REFRESHMENTS.

WELCOME, SIMPSONS FAMILY! FEEL FREE TO MAKE YOURSELVES...

...AT HOME.

GOOD EVENING, HIBBERTS! ALLOW ME TO LIBERATE YOU FROM THESE FATTY TREATS, AS THEY WILL ONLY ADD TO YOUR ALREADY AMPLE HIPS.

¡GASP!¡

NOM! NOM! NOM!

ARRR...HE HAS ALL THE CLASS OF A BLOATED AND BARNACLED NARWHAL, SAYS I!

WORST PARTY GUEST EVER!

BEFORE LONG...

LOOK AT ME! I'M THE GHOST OF FIGGY PUDDING!

HIS BEHAVIOR IS CRIMINAL!

I'M GROWING CHRISTMAS WHISKERS.

♪ ...WE DISH ♪ YOU SOME FAIRY FISHSTICKS AND A FLAPPY POOH BEEEAAAR! ♪

OBVIOUSLY AN ECUMENICAL REWRITE.

OH, MY!

ALL RIGHT! IT'S TIME FOR MY *CHRISTMAS LIMBO!*

≒HRMPH!≒

AHH... MISTLETOE! GET OVER HERE, NEDDY-BOY!

ER...UMMM... ≒GULP!≒

SMOOCH!

≒ERK!≒

WOW! THAT WAS EVEN LONGER THAN *LAST YEAR'S* KISS.

IT'S A NEW RECORD!

UH-OH!

THERE IT IS, LISA! BETTER STOCK UP ON COOKIES. I THINK FLANDERS IS ABOUT TO BLOW!

THAT'S *IT!* YOU ARE WITHOUT A DOUBT THE RUDEST, CRUDEST, MOST APELIKE CREATURE TO *EVER* WALK THE EARTH! YOU HAVE DESTROYED YET *ANOTHER* HOLIDAY GATHERING WITH YOUR BAD MANNERS AND DIMWITTED BARNYARD ANTICS!

HOMER SIMPSON...

...I CAST YOU OUT!

OOHHH...

OHHH...I WAS *TRYING* TO BE GOOD! I REALLY WAS! BUT THE FOOD AND BOOZE WERE JUST *TOO TEMPTING!* CAN I HELP IT IF I'M A BIG GUY WITH BIG APPETITES?

I MUST BE THE *WORST* NEXT-DOOR NEIGHBOR IN THE WORLD! ⁚SNIFF!⁚

I CAN'T BELIEVE FLANDERS CALLED ME AN *APE!*

ACTUALLY, I CALLED YOU AN *APELIKE CREATURE*. MIND IF I SIT A SPELL FOR SOME SHOW-AND-TELL?

IT'S YOUR PICNIC TABLE.

I'M SORRY I WAS A RAGIN' CAJUN EARLIER. THIS IS FOR YOU, HOMER. MERRY CHRISTMAS!

HUH?

BUT I'M YOUR MORTAL FOE, AND I JUST RUINED YOUR PARTY. WHY ARE YOU GIVING ME A PRESENT?

WHY, IT'S AS SIMPLE AS A *NUN'S HABIT,* NEIGHBOR!

WITHOUT YOUR ANTICS, I'D NEVER HAVE A REASON TO CRY OUT TO GOD FOR HELP OR GIVE THE OLD FORGIVENESS MUSCLES MUCH OF A WORKOUT! BEING YOUR NEIGHBOR HAS GIVEN ME EVEN STRONGER BELIEFS... IT'S LIKE I GET TO PASS A *TEST OF FAITH* EVERY DAY!

SO YOU HAVE *ME* TO THANK FOR BEING SO CHURCHY?!

WELL...IN A SENSE. *MERRY CHRISTMAS,* HOMER.

HUH? IT'S EMPTY.

JUST FOR THE MOMENT! FILL THIS BOX WITH SOMETHING YOU'VE BORROWED FROM ME BUT HAVEN'T RETURNED, AND THAT'LL BE MY GIFT TO YOU! MY DVR PLAYER? CORDLESS DRILL? THE FLANDERS' FAMILY FONDUE FUN SET?

HMMM...

THANKS, NED. YOU'VE SHOWN ME THE TRUE REASON FOR THE SEASON.

JUST DOING MY JOB, BUDDY. JUST DOING MY JOB.

HEY, MARGE! FLANDERS JUST SAID THAT I CAN KEEP THE *RIDING LAWN MOWER* I BORROWED AND NEVER GAVE BACK! *WOO-HOO!* I LOVE THAT THING! THIS IS THE BEST CHRISTMAS *EVER!*

OH, DEAR...I HAD FORGOTTEN ABOUT THAT ONE. ⸘SIGH!⸘

THE END

MAYOR MAGGIE

TOM PEYER
SCRIPT

JASON HO
PENCILS

ANDREW PEPOY
INKS

NATHAN HAMILL
COLORS

KAREN BATES
LETTERS

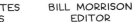
BILL MORRISON
EDITOR

24

29

EYYAAAHHHH!

HOMER?!

TAKE IT *EASY*, HOMIE! EVERYTHING'S ALL RIGHT!

BUT I DREAMED I WAS FEEDING MAGGIE AND SHE FELL ASLEEP AND SHE DREAMED WE WERE ALL BABIES AND SHE WAS THE MAYOR...

...AND SHE WOULDN'T GIVE ME BEER!

MARGE, I HAD NO IDEA SHE WAS SUCH A *POWER TRIPPER!* WE GOTTA *SEND HER AWAY* BEFORE SHE GETS *TOO BIG* AND *STRONG!*

HOMER...

...*BAD DREAMS* ARE JUST WHAT YOU GET WHEN YOU EAT ALL THAT BABY FOOD!

THE END

GRAMPA'S CHRISTMAS ORIGINS
Christmas Eggnog

ERIC ROGERS
SCRIPT

JOHN COSTANZA
PENCILS

PHYLLIS NOVIN
INKS

NATHAN HAMILL/ART VILLANUEVA
COLORS

KAREN BATES
LETTERS

NATHAN KANE
EDITOR

'TISN'T THE SEASON

WELCOME WINTER!

WELCOME, MY FELLOW SPRINGFIELDIANS!

ACCORDING TO OUR CALENDARS OF THE...ER, AH...JULIAN, MAYAN, AND NOVELTY VARIETIES, TODAY MARKS THE *OFFICIAL* START OF WINTER!

AHHH...*THE GREATEST TIME OF THE YEAR!*

BECAUSE OF GOODWILL AND FAMILY TOGETHERNESS?

BETTER! DUFF IS RELEASING THEIR SPECIAL *HOLIDAY BREWS!* LIKE *DUFF GINGERBREAD* AND *DUFF TINSEL!*

WELL, *I'M* WAITING FOR THE ANNUAL WINTER MIGRATION OF THE ELUSIVE *GREEN-FOOTED SANTA FE SPARROW!*

AND IN LESS *BORING* NEWS, I'VE GOT A LOT OF SICK *SLEDDING* TO DO! SNOW, BABY, SNOW!

MAX DAVISON
SCRIPT

MIKE KAZALEH
ART

NATHAN HAMILL
COLORS

KAREN BATES
LETTERS

NATHAN KANE
EDITOR

ONE MONTH LATER...

A BEAUTIFUL SIGHT? ARE WE HAPPY TONIGHT? *HARDLY.*

KENT BROCKMAN HERE, WALKING IN A *WINTER WASTELAND*. IT'S BEEN FOUR WEEKS SINCE THE SEASON BEGAN, AND THERE'S STILL NO SNOWFALL AND PRECIOUS LITTLE HOLIDAY MERRIMENT.

MUCH LIKE *GODOT* OR THE CABLE REPAIRMAN, WINTER IS SIMPLY A *NO-SHOW!* THIS SNOW DEPRIVATION IS AFFECTING THE MOOD OF THE ENTIRE TOWN.

"CHILDREN AREN'T CAROLING..."

♪ JOY TO ♪ THE--

NO. I... I'M NOT FEELING IT.

"...STREETS ARE DEPRIVED OF SNOW ANGELS..."

SO *THIS* IS WHAT A CHESTNUT FEELS LIKE.

SIZZLE!

"...AND UNTOUCHED EGGNOG IS CURDLING BY THE GALLON."

¡GULP!

"METEOROLOGICAL EXPERTS ARE STYMIED."

THERE ARE *ZERO* SCIENTIFIC REASONS WHY THE SEASON IS PASSING US BY...WHAT WITH THE NUMEROUS VARIABLES, OCCLUDED FRONTS, AND GENERAL ‡GA-*HOYVEN*!‡ DON'T LOOK TO *ME* FOR ANSWERS!

STORM TRACKER 3000

SO NOW, THE WORLD'S BRIGHTEST CHRISTMAS TREE SERVES AS A TWISTED REMINDER THAT OUR DAYS MAY INDEED BE BRIGHT...BUT FAR FROM MERRY.

AW, MAN! THIS WEATHER *BITES*!

TELL ME ABOUT IT. NOW WHEN I WEAR MY CHRISTMAS SWEATER, IT JUST SEEMS LAME!

WELL, I'M NOT GOING TO LET THE LACK OF SNOW STOP ME. THAT'S HOW I ROLL!

ONE ILL-ADVISED RUN LATER...

AREN'T YOU GOING TO SAY "HAW HAW"?

IT SOUNDS TOO CLOSE TO "HO! HO! HO!" THE ASSOCIATION BRINGS DOWN MY MOOD.

UGGH...

THAT NIGHT...

I HAVEN'T CHUCKED A SINGLE SNOWBALL! THIS IS THE WORST WINTER EVER!

WELL, THAT'S *NOTHING* COMPARED TO WHAT I WENT THROUGH TODAY...

I AM SORRY, MR. SIMPSON, BUT DUFF HAS STILL NOT DELIVERED ANY OF THEIR HOLIDAY BREWS.

BUT THAT'S WHAT YOU SAID *LAST* MONTH!

FROM WHAT I AM HEARING, THEIR SPECIAL WATER SUPPLY HAS BEEN *CONTAMINATED*.

IS THIS BECAUSE OF THE TIME I WAS AT THE RIVER AND COULDN'T FIND A TREE...?

HOWEVER, THERE IS STILL *REGULAR* DUFF TO PURCHASE!

PSSH! YOU JUST DON'T *GET* CHRISTMAS...DO YOU, APU?

WELL, THE WEATHER MIGHT BE DIFFERENT, BUT IT'S STILL THE HOLIDAY SEASON... WE CAN *STILL* HAVE FAMILY TOGETHERNESS.

RIGHT, MOM?

SIGH! EVERY YEAR SINCE I WAS A LITTLE GIRL I WOULD GO SKATING AND MAKE SNOW ANGELS.

AND STOCKINGS HUNG WITH CARE JUST AREN'T THE SAME WITHOUT A ROARING FIREPLACE!

DAYS LATER...

NOT A SINGLE SANTA FE SPARROW! WHERE *ARE* THEY?

LISA, IT PAINS ME TO SAY, BUT THE SPARROWS AREN'T COMING TO SPRINGFIELD THIS YEAR.

"THEY'RE FLYING INTO SNOWY *SHELBYVILLE* INSTEAD."

SHELBYVILLE CITY LIMITS

LATER...

LOOK AT THIS CITY! WITHOUT THE COMFORTS OF WINTER, IT'S A NIGHTMARE!

THIS ICE IS WET!

RINGFIELD POOL

AW, NUTS! EVERY YEAR ME AN' CARL MAKE SNOWMEN THAT LOOK LIKE US...

...BUT THIS MUD DOESN'T HAVE THE SAME *STRUCTURAL INTEGRITY* AS SNOW.

AND THAT TREE KEEPS MOCKING US WITH ITS BRILLIANT HOLIDAY ENERGY AND GLOW!

I'M *SHAKIN'* WITH RAGE, HERE!

MR. FLANDERS! *YOU* ALWAYS HAVE THE HOLIDAY SPIRIT!

EVEN IF THE TIDE IS OUT, THERE'S STILL *YULETIDE CHEER* AT CASA DE FLANDERS!

HOWEVER...THIS YEAR IT'S TOO WARM FOR *HOT COCOA*, WHICH IS THE ONLY HOT BEVERAGE WE'RE ALLOWED TO IMBIBE.

DADDY SAYS ESPRESSO IS LIQUID BRIMSTONE!

NO SNOW. NO SPARROWS. EVEN "THE HAPPY LITTLE ELVES CHRISTMAS SPECIAL" WAS CANCELED!

SOMEONE IS KEEPING WINTER AWAY FROM SPRINGFIELD... BUT *WHO*?

SIDESHOW BOB! WHAT DO YOU KNOW ABOUT THE MISSING WINTER?

PRECIOUS LITTLE, LISA SIMPSON.

ALAS, I, TOO, AM LAMENTING THE LOSS OF WINTER'S ICY CHILL. NORMALLY, THE SPRINGFIELD POPS PLAY VIVALDI'S *THE FOUR SEASONS*, PARTICULARLY THE STUNNING "WINTER" PORTION.

BUT NOW, THE FOURTH CONCERTO WILL MERELY BE AN EXTENDED "AUTUMN" IN F MAJOR. THE *HEATHENS!*

SNOWDRIFTS ARE AN OPTIMAL LOCATION IN WHICH UNWANTED ASSOCIATES CAN..."DISAPPEAR." THEIR ABSENCE IS MOST REGRETTABLE.

I SEE.

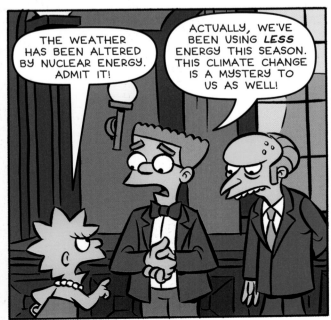

THE WEATHER HAS BEEN ALTERED BY NUCLEAR ENERGY. ADMIT IT!

ACTUALLY, WE'VE BEEN USING *LESS* ENERGY THIS SEASON. THIS CLIMATE CHANGE IS A MYSTERY TO US AS WELL!

HOW DO I KNOW YOU'RE TELLING THE TRUTH?

I'VE TAKEN THE OFFICIAL *MALIBU STACY* *"OATH OF TRUTHFULNESS."* THAT HAS TO STAND FOR SOMETHING, RIGHT?

:SIGH!: OF COURSE. *ALL* SISTERS OF MALIBU STACY ARE HONOR BOUND TO ONE ANOTHER. THANK YOU FOR YOUR TIME.

THAT NIGHT...

IF MY EXTENSIVE READING OF *NANCY DREW MYSTERIES* HAS TAUGHT ME ANYTHING, IT'S THAT THE CULPRIT IS TYPICALLY THE ONE WHO MOST BENEFITS FROM THE CURRENT SITUATION.

BUT WHO CAN THAT BE?

WINTER: WITHOUT YOU

MISSING:
SNOW
BIRDS
HOLIDAY SPIRIT
DAD'S BEER

PRESENT:
GIANT TREE

WAIT! THAT'S *IT*!

PROFESSOR FRINK!

:NNGAAAH!:

I'M LOOKING FOR THE *TRUTH*, PROFESSOR.

NAMELY THE TRUTH ABOUT HOW THE CHRISTMAS TREE IS ABLE TO GLOW SO *UNNATURALLY* BRIGHT!

ME... WELL...I...

ⱢGULP!Ⱡ

ⱢGA-*HOYVEN!*Ⱡ MUCH LIKE A PARTICLE IN A *SINGULARITY'S GRAVITATIONAL PULL,* YOU'VE CAUGHT ME!

THIS IS ALL *MY* FAULT!

"THE GOOD MAYOR ASKED ME TO MAKE SURE THAT OUR TREE WOULD BE *EXTREMELY* BRIGHT THIS YEAR!"

LISTEN UP, FRINKY! I NEED A HOLIDAY SPECTACLE FOR THE...ER, AH...*RECORD BOOKS!* WE NEED THOSE VOTERS TO BE *HOLLY JOLLY* COME ELECTION TIME!

"THIS WAS A PERFECT OPPORTUNITY TO REVEAL THE POWER OF *FRINKIUM NITRATE* TO THE WORLD! IT IS A NEW SOURCE OF VAST, RENEWABLE ENERGY."

THERE IS A *SLIGHT* ISSUE, AS FRINKIUM MAY BE A BIT MORE...HOW DO YOU SAY... *VASTLY RADIOACTIVE* THAN I HAD FIRST ANTICIPATED.

PROFESSOR, WE HAVE TO TAKE THE TREE DOWN AND END THE *OVERLOAD!*

THE NEXT MORNING...

UNFORTUNATELY, MY WELL-INTENTIONED ATTEMPT TO FLOOD THE TOWN WITH *GOOD CHEER* HAS DOOMED US TO... ER, AH...CHRISTMAS OBLIVION.

BOOOOO!

...SO NOW IT BRINGS ME GREAT PLEASURE TO ANNOUNCE THE *TRUE* BEGINNING OF WINTER!

CLICK!

FIZZLE

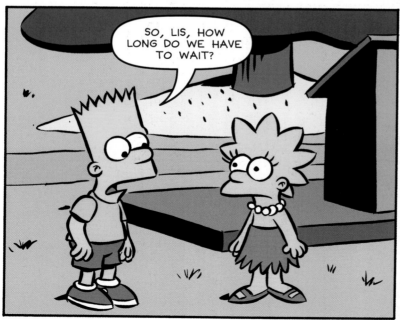

SO, LIS, HOW LONG DO WE HAVE TO WAIT?

YOU NEVER KNOW, BART. WEATHER PATTERNS HAVE BEEN DISRUPTED, AND IT COULD TAKE QUITE A WHILE FOR WINTER TO ROLL IN.

BRRR! WINTER SHOWED UP LATE, BUT IT'S THE LIFE OF THE PARTY.

AHHH... *THAT'S* THE STUFF!

WINTER IS *FINALLY* HERE, DAD!

WELL, NOT FOR *EVERYONE*...

MUCH LIKE DUFFMAN AFTER HIS LATEST BREAKUP, DUFF GINGERBREAD IS *BACK ON THE MARKET!* OH YEAH!

WOO-HOO!

44

FROM THE SECRET FILES OF LISA SIMPSON: "THE CASE OF THE SAX SOLO SABOTEUR"

JAMES W. BATES
SCRIPT

MIKE WORLEY
PENCILS

MIKE ROTE
INKS

ART VILLANUEVA
COLORS

KAREN BATES
LETTERS

BILL MORRISON
EDITOR

HOMIE, HOW COULD YOU EAT A WHOLE PIE? WE WERE GOING TO HAVE THAT ONE AFTER LISA'S BIG CONCERT TOMORROW NIGHT!!

BUT *I* DIDN'T DO IT. I'M *MORE UPSET* THAN *ANYONE* THAT THE PIE IS GONE.

MAYBE *THE DOG* ATE IT!

NO DICE, FAT MAN. SANTA'S LITTLE HELPER WOULD'VE LICKED THE PAN CLEAN.

AND *I* WOULDN'T HAVE?

WHY'S EVERYBODY LOOKING AT ME? I DON'T HAVE *THE ENERGY* TO FIGURE OUT THIS MYSTERY!

IT'S ALL RIGHT, LISA. WE CAN BAKE ANOTHER *CELEBRATION PIE* WHEN YOU GET HOME FROM SCHOOL.

SORRY, MOM, BUT I CAN'T. I HAVE TO *PRACTICE*. I WANT MY *SOLO* TO BE *PERFECT!*

HRMMM...YOU SURE ARE STRESSED OUT ABOUT THAT SOLO. DON'T WORRY, LISA. YOU'RE GOING TO DO *GREAT!*

I WISH I WAS AS CONFIDENT AS YOU ARE, MOM.

THAT AFTERNOON...

SQUEAK!

HONK!

OH NO, *NOT AGAIN!* I'M SO TENSE, I KEEP BREAKING REEDS. I'M *NEVER* GOING TO GET THIS SOLO RIGHT.

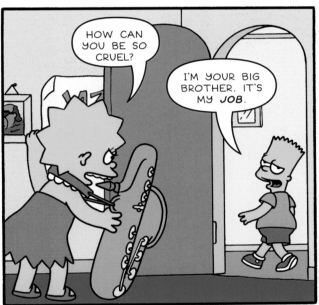

HUH? WHA--?!

WHAT'S IN MY HAIR? AND IN MY SAXOPHONE?

SHAMPOO?!

BART!!!

HOW COULD YOU, BART?

HOW COULD I WHAT?

YOU SAID BEING CRUEL WAS A BIG BROTHER'S JOB.

OH, BART. NEXT THING I KNOW, YOU'LL BE LIKE YOUR FATHER AND BLAME IT ON THE DOG!

I DIDN'T EITHER!

BUT I DIDN'T DO ANYTHING.

FIRST MY PIE AND NOW MY SAXOPHONE! EVERYONE IS DENYING IT, BUT THERE'S A PRANKSTER AFOOT TRYING TO SABOTAGE MY SOLO!

LISA, ALL THE PRESSURE YOU'VE BEEN PUTTING ON YOURSELF TO GET YOUR SOLO RIGHT MUST HAVE CAUSED YOU TO START SLEEPWALKING!

zZZz!

SCREW-UP

HMM. I PRACTICED SO HARD THAT I MADE MYSELF HUNGRY ENOUGH TO EAT A WHOLE PIE IN MY SLEEP...

...AND I WAS SO WORRIED ABOUT LOOKING GOOD ON STAGE THAT I POURED SHAMPOO INTO MY SAXOPHONE.

MOM, I WAS SO CONCERNED THAT I WAS GOING TO RUIN THE CONCERT THAT I WROTE THE WORDS "SCREW UP" ACROSS MY FOREHEAD.

NOW YOU LISTEN TO ME, YOUNG LADY. I'M GOING TO SHOW YOU THE *REAL TRUTH*.

WATCH THIS VIDEO OF YOUR *LAST CONCERT!*

LISA'S CHRISTMAS CONCERT

I WAS *REALLY GOOD*.

SEE? YOU HAVE NOTHING TO BE WORRIED ABOUT. YOU ARE A *WONDERFUL MUSICIAN*, AND YOU ARE GOING TO BE *TERRIFIC* TONIGHT!

NOW YOU TAKE A LITTLE NAP BEFORE THE CONCERT AND DREAM ABOUT HOW WELL YOU'RE GOING TO PLAY.

THANKS, MOM.

SCREW-UP

THE END

52

THIS IS GOING TO BE THE BEST CHRISTMAS TREE EVER!

IF ONLY OUR *MODEL* WOULD HOLD STILL...

BUT MY ARMS ARE TIRED AND THESE LIGHTS ARE BURNING MY SKIN!

GRAMPA, WE HAVE TO PRACTICE DECORATING *YOU*, SO WE CAN DO THE *REAL* TREE LATER!

WHY DON'T YOU DISTRACT YOURSELF BY TELLING US HOW *CHRISTMAS TREES* CAME TO BE?

GRAMPA'S CHRISTMAS ORIGINS
Christmas Trees

"IT ALL BEGAN WHEN *MARCO POLO* RETURNED TO ITALY AFTER HIS EXPEDITION TO CHINA..."

THESE *FIREWORKS* ARE GONNA BE A REAL HIT WITH THE GANG BACK HOME!

TOO BAD I COULD ONLY PLUNDER *ONE* FOR EACH OF MY FRIENDS. AH, NO WORRIES. I'M SURE THEY'LL UNDERSTAND THE VALUE OF AUSTERITY.

"BACK IN ITALY..."

IT'S CHRISTMAS TIME, POLO. HAND OVER OUR GIFTS FROM AFAR! AND THERE'D BETTER BE *PLENTY* OF 'EM!

DON'T CUT US OFF AFTER ONLY ONE!

UHH...LET ME GO GET 'EM FOR YA...

GEEZ. MAYBE I SHOULD MAKE LIKE THE GUYS IN CHINA AND KEEP MY STUFF HIDDEN BEHIND A GIANT WALL!

"BUT SINCE HE COULDN'T FIND A GREAT WALL TO PROTECT HIS GOODS..."

"...HE USED A *GREAT WALNUT TREE!*"

I'LL JUST BURY THESE HERE AND GIVE THOSE GUYS AN I.O.U. OR SOMETHIN'.

MATT GROENING

ERIC ROGERS & MAX DAVISON
SCRIPT

JOHN COSTANZA
PENCILS

PHYLLIS NOVIN
INKS

ART VILLANUEVA
COLORS

KAREN BATES
LETTERS

NATHAN KANE
EDITOR

EVAN DORKIN
SCRIPT

DEXTER REED
PENCILS

MIKE ROTE
INKS

NATHAN HAMILL
COLORS

KAREN BATES
LETTERS

BILL MORRISON
EDITOR

THE END

HOLE LOTTA TROUBLE

IAN BRILL
SCRIPT

NINA MATSUMOTO
PENCILS

ANDREW PEPOY
INKS

NATHAN HAMILL
COLORS

KAREN BATES
LETTERS

NATHAN KANE
EDITOR

GOOD ARM, MILHOUSE! I GOTTA SAY, I'M SURPRISED.

THANKS, BART. IT'S A NICE CHANGE OF PACE TO *NOT* BE THE TARGET FOR ONCE!

AAAH!!

PAF!

BART! *HELP!*

SORRY, FRIEND. IN A *SNOWBALL FIGHT,* IT'S EVERY KID FOR HIMSELF. OR HERSELF. NO NEED TO DISCRIMINATE.

WHOA! I THINK I JUST SPOTTED THE MOTHER OF ALL *TACTICAL ADVANTAGES!*

THE DIGGING TOOLS...

MARTIN'S PRIZED SHOEHORN AND POCKET PROTECTOR.

MILHOUSE'S "SMALL WONDER" POG AND PICTURE OF HIS MOTHER.

BART'S PUDDING CUP SPOON AND CHROMIUM RADIOACTIVE MAN TRADING CARD.

OKAY, HERE'S THE PLAN...

WE SHOULD GET A HOSE AND TOTALLY SOAK THOSE TWERPS IN THE PIT!

HA...YEAH! WE'LL MAKE SOME *TWERPSICLES!*

WHAT TH--?!

PAF!

WHAT THE CRUD?

HOW'D HE GET OUT?

HOW ABOUT A FROZEN DINNER, JERKS!

DEAN RANKINE
STORY & ART

KAREN BATES
LETTERS

NATHAN KANE
EDITOR

THE END

HE'S BACK!

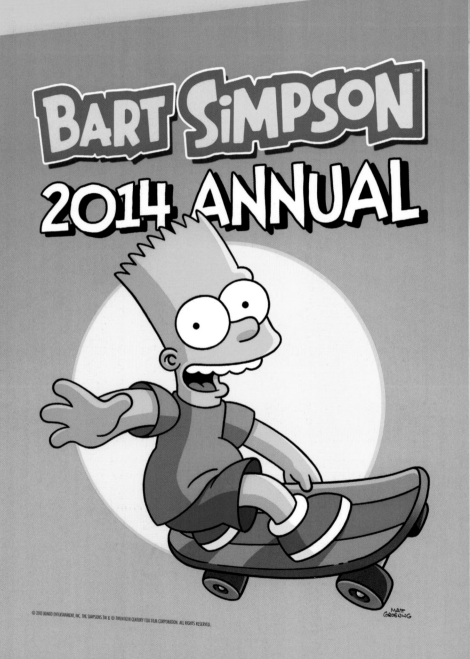

THE BRAND NEW COMIC COLLECTION, AVAILABLE FROM ALL GOOD BOOKSTORES AND ONLINE RETAILERS!

BART SIMPSON 2014 ANNUAL

TITAN BOOKS
A WORLD OF ENTERTAINMENT

www.titanbooks.com